The 1st Treasury

Farcus® is distributed internationally by Universal Press Syndicate.

For information, write Andrews and McMeel, a Universal Press Syndicate Company, 4900 Main Street, Kansas City, Missouri 64112.

The creators of Farcus® can be contacted at Farcus Cartoons Inc.
e-mail: 74777.3301@compuserve.com
Internet: http://hypernet.on.ca/farcus

ISBN: 0-8362-0779-3
Library of Congress Catalog Card Number: 95-77567

The 1st Treasury

By David Waisglass and Gordon Coulthart

Andrews and McMeel
A Universal Press Syndicate Company
Kansas City

Foreword

by Lynn Johnston

When I was about 10, I guess, I began to buy cartoon books for my father. Thus, I managed to acquire for myself the collected works of some of the finest cartoonists of the day … while appearing to spend my allowance generously on someone else.

Fortunately, Dad was as consumed with comics as I was, and one of the artists most revered by us both was Virgil Partch. With a few wriggling lines, he could produce a profile that captured a comedic expression like no other cartoonist on the planet. His line was his signature, and his ahead-of-his-time humor was unique. His work was unparalleled until, perhaps, now.

No cartoonist ever wants to be compared to someone else. Indeed, we all have a message and style of line that's uniquely our own. I do want to say, however, that not since Virgil Partch's "Brackets" have I seen such an easy, unbroken line, flowing up, down and around some of the funniest expressions possible.

With its uncluttered style, Farcus is a rare example of less being more. Much more! David Waisglass and Gordon Coulthart have created an unlimited cast of moronic characters happily placed in ludicrous situations. The result is pure Farcus.

I caught my first glimpse of their original comic art on the "gag wall" of an animation studio in Ottawa, where Gordon was working. "That's really funny! You should be syndicated," I informed him. "We are," he replied modestly. "We sort of syndicated ourselves."

Indeed, they were self-syndicated to a few dozen newspapers. Within six months, Farcus surpassed its promising beginnings, and is now distributed by Universal Press Syndicate to more than 200 newspapers and is rapidly winning more.

You are about to experience *The 1st Treasury of Farcus*. Prepare to enjoy yourself. Prepare to see yourself.

David Waisglass and Gordon Coulthart have opened one more window into the two dimensional pen-and-ink fantasy world we call "the comics" … and, something insanely wonderful is looking back!!!

Virgil Partch would have approved.

Lynn Johnston, Creator
For Better or For Worse®

"It says, 'Best before November 17'."

"It makes you miss the old punch clock, doesn't it?"

"Relax! It'll be here any minute."

Bob finally gets the recognition he deserves.

"Seeing you brought the gun, Norman, why don't *you* start the meeting?"

"I'll need to see you and your offspring for the next two million years."

"We'll take 'em."

"I don't know ... somehow I thought it would be different."

"I don't understand ... it works on paper."

"It keeps our insurance premiums down."

"Face it, Don. We're losers."

"Care to make a donation to a non-profitable corporation?"

"Oh geez, not another mission statement."

"Say, what sort of headhunting firm is this?"

"Damn! I left a Kleenex in my pocket."

"I'm afraid, Hedgewood, you haven't really grasped the concept here."

"I don't think it heard you ... say it louder."

"It's obvious, Steeves, no one has worked harder for this promotion than you."

"Work with me, will ya? ... This is front page material!"

BACK SEAT DRIVING SCHOOL

WAISGLASS/COULTHART

"... and now I'd like to discuss new ways to fight our absenteeism problem."

"Before you go, could you tell me where you put the Kenshaw file?"

"Why yes, we do have something available next Thursday."

"I assume we get time-and-a-half for working Sundays."

"Hey, look — a perfectly good manager!"

"I think we went too far."

"He's been like this since he got his promotion."

"It's an all-new environmentally enriched organic food by-product that has revolutionized lawn care!"

"Don't worry, I do my best work at the last minute."

"Geez, these drugstore fliers are becoming a real nuisance."

"We're looking for someone with a little less experience."

"It makes kind of a growling sound."

After teaching first-year Physics for 25 years, Professor Morgan takes a temporary leave from his faculty.

"Frankly, this works just as well."

"Still haven't figured out how to send e-mail, huh, Bob?"

"What d'ya mean, you don't need any consultants?"

"Don't sell your shares yet, Harry ... pet rocks are a long-term investment."

"... and he's got leadership potential."

"He dashed out of cubicle four without signaling!"

"Psst ... Harry, does our benefit plan cover this?"

"My new boss is a control freak."

"Well, we've worked out the details. Now, if we can just agree on the main points ..."

"Send in Furlow. I have some numbers to run by him."

"If pigs could fly ..."

"Say, do we get Labor Day off?"

"Take it from me, pal — you don't have to follow the herd."

"That's it — no more free coffee."

"I hear there's an opening on the 22nd floor."

"There's a foursome at Fifth and 34th who want to play through."

"... and without nuclear physics, we wouldn't be here today."

"Can't you file a grievance like everyone else?"

"Microwave is more efficient."

"Just be yourself."

"We don't get much business, but we fill an important niche."

"Quit complaining! Times are hard, and we've got to be versatile."

"It's our new telephone system! Notice how long the string is this time."

"Oh yeah? Well my dad won more employee awards than your dad!"

"So, what's it like working out of your home?"

"I'm not sure, but I think they want us to pee on this stuff."

"Harris, you're taking my open door policy a bit too far."

"I've got to find a job that's more politically correct."

"Oh look, honey, she drew an organization chart!"

WAISGLASS/COULTHART

"Don't worry, Jimmy. If there's fish in this lake, we'll find them."

"I wasn't gonna ask him to move!"

"There's no message attached to this one, Sir."

"Maybe it's time you took a break from Juvenile Court."

"What began with a few pencils and paper clips ..."

"And you thought they didn't care."

**"Out of the way, farm boy!
We want what's in the silo."**

"I'll trade my bologna for your tuna fish?"

"Of course they're 100% pure beef — it's a condition of my parole."

"Hey, that looks like one of those letter bombs!"

"No matter what I say, these farmers can't keep their hands off me."

"I'd like to start my own business ... but, frankly, I think it's too risky."

"You're right, we did have enough paper clips."

"Yes, Morris, I heard about your promotion."

"Don't worry about it, kid. This is Hell. You don't have to go outside to smoke."

"I don't mind the 'no frills' therapy, but maybe you could buy a couch?"

"See if they'll settle for acknowledgment."

"$365? Sounds fair to me."

"He's been taking a crisis management course."

"Frankly, I didn't think they'd go for this stuff."

"And it gets worse ... they lost my luggage too!"

"You see, son, this way we can spend more time together."

"I still don't think he'll give us business cards."

"The kids want to know what's next on the agenda."

"Ms. Kelsey, did you get rid of that salesman yet?"

"How many times do I have to tell you? ... Don't draw on the walls!"

"Do you have anything in a pump?"

"We don't have union support on this one."

"After all, Freemont ... a deadline is a deadline."

Why socially conscious businesses never last.

"I'm telling ya, honey, any bozo can run this company."

"Ms. Spencer is here for her assertiveness training."

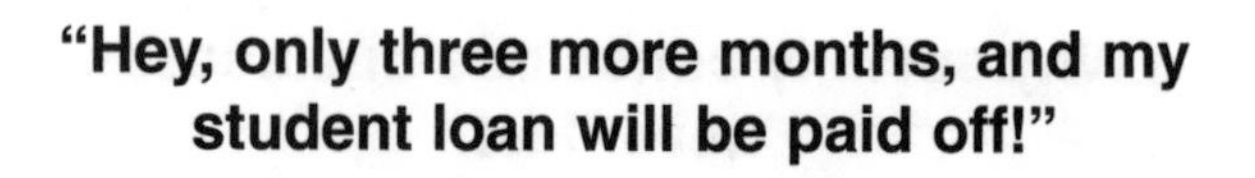

"Hey, only three more months, and my student loan will be paid off!"

"Wow, this must be some sort of record — a full day's shift and not one weirdo!"

"Last cigarette? They told me this was a taste test!"

"We have to let you go, Grimsby — you've got too much charm and charisma for this line of work."

"It's our new computer security system!"

"And what exactly did you do at the Funky Chicken Credit Union?"

"My client refuses to answer on the grounds that he may incriminate me."

"Hello, photocopy repair?"

"Greg never got around to reading all of his memos on Friday."

"I preferred the course on looting and pillaging."

No class travel.

"This is my boss's idea of a raise."

"Nonsense ... after 25 years, you deserve it!"

"Okay, for the last time — waiters get 15%, bellmen get a dollar per bag ..."

"For $10,000, I can sell you a franchise."

"What did you expect? You hired a turtle!"

"I don't see why we pay more for fewer calories."

"I thought you said you had a home theater system."

"Damn spare!"

"My prognosis? Thank goodness! I thought it was our sales picture."

"Maybe you should find another activity to help you unwind."

"We've been robbed!"

"Sorry, Frank, but we're cracking down on people who leave work early."

"Think of it as a payroll deduction."

"My card."

"Don't take it personally — a lot of people are lactose intolerant."

"At least you got the job security you wanted."

"Okay, okay. No more Japanese management seminars."

"Next time we cruise for babes, we'll take my car."

"White sugar?! Are you nuts? That stuff can kill you."

"I can start next week, if I don't find anything better."

"You said we should be more competitive."

"It's always something ... mittens, boots, hats. I'm telling you, you'd lose your head if it wasn't screwed on!"

"Uh, not you, Bob ... I meant *other* people can't take criticism."

"Remember, kid, I've got seniority."

"I want an eight percent increase in my allowance and a benefit plan."

"It does multiple graphs and my shorts at the same time."

"Why me? I didn't do anything."

WAISGLASS/COULTHART

"Then, I said, 'Why go to a big city when everything we need is right here in the pasture?' But, nooo ..."

"Crumbs were much bigger before the recession."

"Too salty?! Hey, I put a lot of sweat and tears into making this!"

"It's part of the creative process."

"So, what's it like being the only man on our management team."

"And it runs on remote control!"

"I hate these elevator music gigs."

"Quick, somebody hire a temp!"

"What d'ya suppose it means?"

"May I see your boarding pass?"

"... and then he suggested a career in the public service."

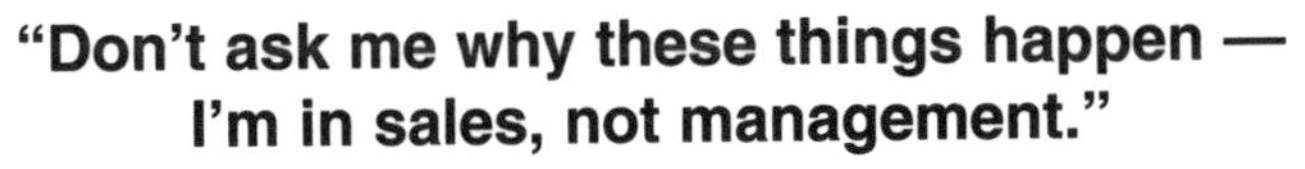
"Don't ask me why these things happen —
I'm in sales, not management."

"Hey look! I've been invited to a roast!"

"Things aren't working out here, Edwards.
Have you considered a job with
our competition?"

"Your Honor, my client, Flamo the
Magnificent, is no threat to society."

"I knew flexible hours wouldn't work."

"I think you should forget about this organic shampoo idea."

"I guess this ends our round table discussion."

"If your house burns down, we'll replace the defective unit absolutely free!"

"I know it's tradition, Nick — but you can't discriminate against tall people anymore."

"If at first you don't succeed, embezzle."

"You're late, Bizley. And that ax murderer excuse won't work this time."

"I assume you're not the primary care giver."

"It's our new image, Nick."

"You know, there's a cafeteria downstairs."

"Say, we're looking for someone with your skills in our collections department."

"It's a routine operation, but we want you to pay in advance just to be on the safe side."

"Okay, so what else does it do?"

"Honest, my name *is* Howard Johnson!"

"So, what makes you so damn special?"

"... commitment to quality ... commitment to quality ..."

"Trust me, kid, you don't get this kind of experience in journalism school."

"It will help you to read between the lines."

"Well, okay, but I need three pieces of identification."

"Actually, I'm not your secretary. I'm the Second Assistant for the Apprentice in Training to the Executive's Chief Aide."

"I should have taken the watch."

"Geez, I don't know how we ever did it without a strategic plan."

"He's right. The law says we have to negotiate in good faith."

"It contains 68 million excuses."

"Okay, we're out. Now what?"

"We were robbed last week."

"Okay, okay ... but it's my turn next!"

"Excuse me, Your Honor, but I believe I was here first."

"It'll cut down on the number of work breaks!"

"I'm not really awake until I've had 32 cups of coffee."

"I'm telling ya, these are the first signs of inflation."

"He still thinks he can get promoted."

"Say, I thought this was a management washroom."

"I'm sorry, we don't stuff lawyers here."

"They don't bite unless you use fifties."

"What does the flashing red light mean?"

"Say, is this in our job description?"

"Let's get it right this time — booty means *riches,* not *footware*!"

"Good news, Smitsberg! The boss agrees you deserve a bigger paycheck."

"Henderson, I think you misunderstood our dress code."

"Stop complaining. You're going first class."

"We've had a few drive-bys, but no serious offers."

"According to our tests, you've got rigor mortis."

"It's not so bad when you look at it from this angle."

"Real estate!"

"I'm sure it won't be a problem ... you fellas look like a good risk to me."

"Performance reviews are much more effective this way."

"Psst. 'Union,' pass it on."

"I told you we'd get a dental plan."

"It seems you have a problem with authority figures."

WAISGLASS/COULTHART

"Bently, you idiot! I said hire a *paralegal*."

"We try to save something for the environment."

"Can you see the serial number from where you are?"

"This isn't the drug testing program I had in mind."

When stress management works too well.

"I hate when they give us junk bonds."

"They counter-offered with 10 *suggestions* and want a guarantee on the promised land thing."

"Paper or plastic bags?"

"Tonight's scores — owners $48 million, players $32 million."

"Careful, guys, I've seen this scam before."

"Then it's agreed ... there's no room for further cuts in production."

"No thanks, it gives me heartburn."

"Okay, now explain to me again what my motivation is for this scene."

"I'm just a figurehead — the real business is in Taiwan."

"How much is it to fly nonstop?"

"Your father wonders why you don't play with your club anymore?"

"How long have you been on the surplus list?"

"Listen to the customer, Greenham. But don't take no for an answer."

"That's the third smoker we've lost this week."

"They laid off the horses last week."

"Your Honor, this man unjustly characterized my client as being naughty."

"... and transfer this to my account."

"If we were unionized, we wouldn't have to settle for crumbs."

"We cut out the middleman."

"I was right — they can't legally fire me!"

"I know this scam ... once you cut it, I have to keep coming back."

"It appears you misunderstood when I asked you to organize this department."

"Mr. Simms is our new quality control supervisor."

"I told you this chimp was trouble."

"Remember, you need a note from the doctor."

"I'm not sure, but I'd say it's job burn out."

"Nonsense — it only *seems* like eternity."

"Greetings. We seek new markets."

"We couldn't find the best candidate for the position, so we'll promote you instead."

"So, how long did you work at the Ms. Gooey Cookie Factory."

"C'mon in, Harvey. I found a way to settle this grievance."

"I suggest you start small ... you can always upgrade later."

"Geez, Harry, just once I'd like to go somewhere without you looking like a tourist."

"I'm sorry, sir, but $5,000 to bribe a city official is illegal, immoral and totally inadequate."

"Of course I know the penalty for perjury, but I'd be in more trouble if I told the truth."

"Will somebody turn down the damn air conditioner?!"

"Do you have other references besides Snake and Butthead."

"The marriage is invalid because I was insane when I married him."

"Honey, have you seen the remote control?"

"If you learned from your mistakes, Carl, you'd be a genius."

"If it looks like a duck, walks like a duck..."

"We've had a few complaints about your recruitment methods."

"There are two types of people in this world ... those who generalize and those who don't."

“Okay. You’ve got 15 minutes! What’s wrong with me?”

"Uh-oh, Harold's getting another fax."

"Some days, I just don't feel good about this job."

"Some people think you're taking advantage of our family benefits."

"There's still no conclusive evidence that it's a health risk."

"I wouldn't be so paranoid, if everyone wasn't out to get me."

"Tell me things went well in Chicago, Rimstead."

"Damn it, Brimsby. Keep still."

"I'm okay ... see? Nothing's broken!"

"It seems to me, Fleming, you have the skills we want on our management team."

“Maybe this job-sharing plan wasn’t a good idea.”

“Can’t you see we’ve been domesticated?”

“I understand, but I would hardly call the summer months unconstitutional.”

“And I won this for winning so many awards!”

Dexter Ringwall creates the X-91
in his own image.

"It says here, you have a greater chance
of being struck by lightning than
winning the lottery."

"I still don't see how this was a
work-related accident.

"This electric car was not one of your
better ideas."

"Try to think of this as a government job."

"... and he was in charge of employee morale."

"I don't think it's a good idea we go into business together."

"We're capitalist pigs, son — there's no reason to be ashamed of it."

"What about the rest of my lesson?!"

"Your horse refuses to come out until he talks to a union representative."

"Hey! How about you be the anchor for a while?"

"It's decaf, and no one could tell the difference."

"C'mon guys. We'll never get this done if you don't stop running around."

"You know, just once I wish he'd say *please*."

"Good luck, Eddie."

"I can put it in a sandwich, but it'll cost more."

"My wife thinks I'm a workaholic."

"Wow! This is the biggest iron deposit I've ever seen."

Breakfast with an engineer.

"I trusted him more when he had a whip."

The first organization chart.

"You mean you didn't know this was a seasonal job?"

"Well, this finalizes your legal separation ..."

"Okay, on the count of three, everyone yells 'boo' ..."

"... and then they cut my travel allowance."

"Funny thing, Dalton — your request for a transfer suddenly came through."

"Some of the guys in the flock think you're a bit of a show-off."

"So, you're the new ideas man …"

"Trust me, kid. Keep your mouth shut and let them sleep in."

"Give me three large bass ... and don't bother to wrap them."

Early map-making techniques.

"Uh, no, that's the employees' smoking lounge."

"It's the sixth planet past the sun ... you can't miss it."

"Say, Ed, how long have you been on nights?"

"Yeah, yeah, the check's in the mail."

"Well, frankly ... it's your attitude."

"In local news ... employees at Buxley's Dry Cleaners are still on strike."

"We charge by the snowflake."

"Let me guess — you've been transferred from Research and Development."

"Yeah, but I'm down to one pack a day."

"Okay, now bring it down slowly."

"It's a worker exchange program. The old guy is grazing in the back 40."

"Yeah, this time I told the secretarial pool to send me a real knock out."

"I'm telling you, people really go for this stuff."

"There's no sex discrimination here because we fired all the men."

"I'm not blaming you, Lewis. I'm delegating responsibility."

"They're going back to Personnel."

"No matter what I do, I still only produce 2%."

"The cook wants to know if you have any next of kin."

"I don't get it. We've checked every circuit and it still won't boot."

"Next time, let's get a car with a passenger-side air bag."

"Okay, that's good. Now smile ..."

"How long have you been a member of Smokers Anonymous?"

"It all started with a few bones and a pair of slippers ..."

"It worked, didn't it?"

"We also carry orange, wild cherry and wintergreen mint."

"Nobody takes these security cameras seriously."

"Does it come on disk?"

"Put the money in the bag, or the kid starts playing."

"Tell me about your first program."

"Scotty, here, says you're three weeks behind on his allowance."

"Hey look, Spriggs ... this moron left his keys in the car!"

Near the end, Lloyd could read the writing on the wall.

"We'd like a table near a waiter."

"No need to worry, Milrod. We all make mistakes."

"For a reduced fine, I'll give you the names of three speeders and a litter bug."

"... now let's see how you react to scenes of your employees leaving early."

"All in favor of shooting that duck ..."

"I know he's a parrot — but he's the only witness who hasn't sold his story to *Hard Copy*."

"Gee, things *are* getting tight around here."

"We're out of napkins."

"Don't bother to thank me, I needed the practice."

"Funny how it breaks every morning at 7:15."

"It's your office. They want to know if you can stay home a few more days."

"Never ask about the severance pay."

"You gave away 60 billion toys and didn't get one receipt?!"

"Here, Section 4A, 'Man's Best Friend' ... it doesn't say anything about fetching."

"I need fire insurance, quick!"

"What's to know? Give 'em a lullaby, some formula, and before you know it — you've got a footprint on the bottom line!"

"Hey, fellas, the grass *does* look greener on the other side."

"The dog ate it."

"Trainees."

"Your 10:00 marketing meeting was rained out."

"You were the best P.R. man we ever had."

"I was cleaning it."

"I need another $50."

"You can't plead insanity."

WAISGLASS/COULTHART

"... but the salesman said it was a universal remote."

"Dad says, 'Get a job.' — but being a leech is all I know!"

"Say, haven't I met some of you before?"

"They've joined the free-range movement."

"Faulkner, here, got a government grant to study the effects of UV rays."

"It's an old idea, but damned if it doesn't work."

"All that training for a lousy desk job."

"It comes with the promotion, Ralph — the car, secretary and new friends."

"You didn't think jumping out of a 10-story building would get rid of me, did you?"

"Has it been six months already?"

"I'm sorry, Mr. Grimswell, you can't write off your son as a loss."

"It's a convenience store."

"And would you say our service was courteous and friendly?"

"Gesundheit."

"Maybe you should just wake up earlier."

"Don't ask if they're fresh."

"There, I think he sees us now."

"We installed some new equipment in your office while you were away."

"Whose stupid idea was it to take over a tar company!"

Before fridge magnets.

"A few more copies and they'll be done."

"It seems to me this company lacks leadership."

"Now remember, when he calls you 'dear' ... take him out."

"Sure, we'll tell you the location of the new office. Just give us a few more days."

"You can't divorce your wife just because she refuses to laugh at your jokes."

"Does it come in a pastel?"

"Hold on, the ball is coming."

"I don't mind having multiple personalities — the problem is I hate crowds."

"I hate junk mail."

"Hi. My name is Dave, and I'm member #378-FC/29-Y87."

"Gentlemen, I propose we buy the Wig World Toupee Company."

"I guess it wasn't a good idea to scale down just before Christmas."

"Remember when all we had to do was fetch?"

"Sorry, Grimsby, this is a smoke-free workplace."

"Stop worrying about doing a good job — the big money is in severance pay!"

"I don't have any emotional problems ... can I borrow some of yours?"

"If you don't like it, see the machine on the sixth floor."

"All those in favor of making a decision ..."

"I've seen this before ... Just don't open the trunk."

"I'm confused — if we date, is that harassment or overtime?"

"I think I finally found a no-smoking program that works."

"Geez, I hate these employee motivation seminars."

"Bently, here, has been the scapegoat for some of the top companies in America."

"C'mon sister, don't believe everything you read."

"Management thinks I can offer a new perspective."

"It's not a bribe — but let's just say there's plenty more where that came from."

"Because I'm the boss, that's why!"

"Of course I'm qualified ... I've had hundreds of jobs like this!"

"Okay, Babstock, this time you can make the siren noise."

"They said it was a health club."

"It costs a little more, but it'll pay for itself in six months!"

"Don't see your dog around, Mr. Morriscey. Guess I put a scare into him yesterday."

"Well, at least you got over your fear of heights!"

"I bought it on an installment plan."

"You were caught sleeping on the job again, Dexter."

"That's *Dr.* Idiot to you."

"I don't know … last time I saw Binkman, he was surfing the Net."

"I will not resign. I will not resign. I will not …"

"Okay, now add the 'pinch of salt' …"

"Would you like another finger bowl?"

"One more time — row, row, row your boat ..."

"Love the idea, Bingham. But where do we get the tiny workers?"

"Painting helps me loosen up."

"I quit. You guys give me the willies."

"Looks like a slow news day."

"It may be a power surge."

"And how do I know it isn't stolen?"

"Okay, Eddie, you can go home now."

"We've had a few complaints that you're not a team player."

"Three more cases and we'll have enough for payroll."

"With this little gizmo, collateral isn't necessary."

"You know the rules, Bizwell — no personal items on the desk!"

"I suggested he pursue his dream."

"I told you not to drink so much."

"Say, didn't I vote for you last year."

"We'll see lower interest rates overnight, and a higher dollar by the weekend."

"At Hogwell Industries, every employee is entitled to three weeks' paid vacation."

"Do not light barbecue before reading page six."

"We couldn't afford a photographer."

"The bank repossessed your condo."

"You can use Hobson's desk. He won't be in today."

"Say, while you're up there ..."

"And this is the ulcer I got on the Kenshaw account."

"Forgive me, Father, for I have mismanaged."

"Don't expect warm and fuzzy platitudes around here, Fishbeck."

"There's nothing worse than bad imitation crab."

"See, I told you we wouldn't be safe from insurance salesmen."

"Sure, I have a last request … fire my lawyer."

"I should have worn flats."

"There ... just between the Big Dipper and the Pepsi ad."

"... Are you trying to tell me I'm fired?"

"It's okay to be sympathetic, but don't actually help anyone."

"Are you Al?"

"It's a 30,000-page study that proves we don't need to change the way we work."

"Yes, it is a nasty paper cut, but you don't qualify for handicapped parking."

"You love your work more than me."

"Gentlemen, I suggest we stop promoting managers on the basis of seniority."

"He's our new high-speed copier."

"And you thought they wouldn't give us an exercise room."

"We've got too many damn bureaucrats! Prepare a requisition for more people to study the problem."

"Okay, now let me get this straight — it's a last-minute sell-off and no singles allowed."

"Frankly, Bob, we were expecting a more detailed sales plan."

"I remember when a simple water balloon would satisfy you."

"I quit my last job because everyone there hated my guts."

"Do you have anything for twisted, meanspirited, overbearing supervisors?'

"I need the overtime."

"Hey, look guys! The company is gonna build us an exercise room."

"I don't think reverse psychology is gonna work."

"He can't come to the phone. He's studying for a stress management course."

"It's wedged in there tight, Mr. Mayor. But it's not as bad as last time."

"I see this isn't the first time you've been charged with contempt."

"Do you ever wonder what they put in these things?"

"It seems you misunderstood when I said to visualize the audience naked."

"Would you like a gun with that?"

"... and this is our corporate planning group."

"If this is a fake, I'm gonna sue."

"... and in this one, I keep all our foreign investment."

"Okay, but don't tell anyone ... you know how rumors get started."

"Hey, wait a minute ... only a man would wear green pumps with a blue chiffon dress!"

EMPLOYEE TRAINING

WAISGLASS/COULTHART

"First, we teach the basics ..."

"And on Tuesdays they go to ASPCA meetings."

"I'm just gonna pick up a few things for dinner."

"Sorry, Earl, but that's all the budget allows for our witness protection program."

"Management says our coffee breaks are too long."

"Just what I've always wanted — an in-ground pool table."

"He wants me to thaw him when the recession is over."

"Cool! I just jammed the air traffic control tower!"

"For a few dollars more, I can put you in an air-cushioned Nike."

"It's not easy ordering layoffs ... but I guess that's why they pay me $8.3 million a year."

"Duffy sure has a way with visual aids."

"No, Fifi ... the mouse. Get the mouse!"

"We want employees who give 100% of themselves."

"Vegetarians give me gas."

"Our day-care program offers parents a better return on investment."

"And this one is really scary ... this guy accidentally files a T-81 without completing Section 31."

How Vincent van Gogh really lost his ear.

"They liked my proposal, but suggested I leave Teddy at home."

"Yes, we do have a minority hiring program ... why do you ask?"

"We're trying to reduce the paperwork."

"After 25 years of loyal service, all I have is a crummy gold watch and $3 million in office supplies."

"Your insurance covers only our cheapest bypass valves."

ALL YOU CAN EAT BUFFET

WAISGLASS/COULTHART

"This is Rex. He's been hired through our affirmative action program."

"I don't know what to make of this, Tom — it's a recommendation from our competitor."

"It's supposed to improve morale."

"I don't want to mention any names, but one of us is on a diet!"

"Sorry, Henry, maybe the car pool won't be so crowded tomorrow."

"It's clearly a conflict of interest. I strongly advise against accepting any more milk and cookies."

"Unfortunately, the health and safety committee doesn't meet until next Friday."

"I think you're getting too comfortable in your position here, Wilson."

"Hey, Vinnie, wake up. The boss wants to know if you're willing to work overtime."

"They're right, Ralph — we have to give them two weeks notice."

"No need to worry, Ms. Harris.
We fixed the leak."

"Even though we're shipwrecked with no chance of survival, I'm still your boss!"

"This is our paper cut clinic."

"Now remember, it's a trick question if they ask what kind of idiot are you."

"Don't take this personally."

"I hate Christmas. All this smiling makes my face hurt."

"Just say I need plenty of rest and sunshine."

"And this slightly used paper clip is a token of our appreciation."

"Look, Mom! I made all the phones cordless."

"I don't think our employees should be training these robots."

"I can't find a position to suit my lifestyle."

"It looks like a problem with your undercarriage."

"Watch what you say — this room may be bugged."

"Let me get this straight — the only thing this committee has decided is to form a new committee."

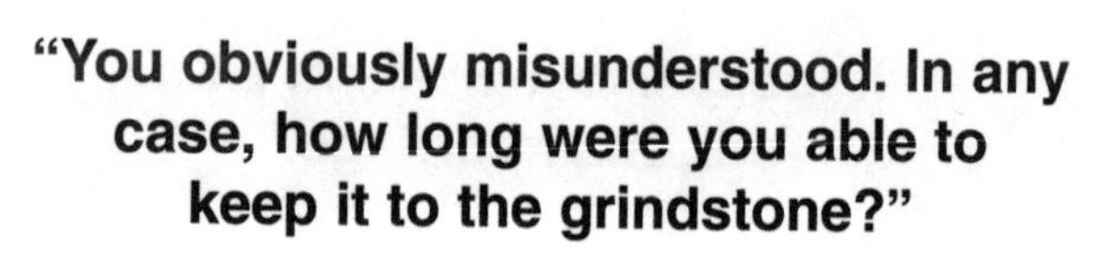

"You obviously misunderstood. In any case, how long were you able to keep it to the grindstone?"

"Well, actually, this is the first time I've used a computer dating service."

"The gun shop is on the second floor — this is the toy department."

"How's my appeal going?"

"Quick, I need 10,000 more temps!"

"I'm tellin' ya, honey, I'll never have to buy another suit."

"I know it's from the cafeteria, but this isn't the turnover we wanted you to study."

"My accountant says I'm a rich man trapped in a poor man's body."

WAISGLASS/COULTHART

"Rumor has it, Filman, you've taken a second job."

"I'm not sure — maybe this *is* his analysis of the west coast market."

"Yes, sir, I believe we have our costs under control."

"You know, I really respect the way you spoke up when they asked for your opinion."

"We value underlings like you, Grimsby, because they know their place."

"It's only until the postage meter is repaired."

"I still don't see how dressing up makes it a white-collar crime."

"Why do I always get the tough districts?"

"The Law Review said I'm negligent. Is that good or bad?"

"His brother knows the owner."

"It's a petition of some sort, but I can't make out this chicken scrawl."

"Once these guys find out where you live, there's no getting rid of them."

"You're not getting my lunch money any more."

"Our video monitoring system lets you avoid annoying sales calls."

"It's for the home business market. It gives you the illusion of working in a crowded noisy office!"

"This was the only drug rehabilitation center I could afford."

"Thank you for your résumé and ... oh, I see you attached your sick mother's X-rays."

"This time we strike! Last year's slowdown was a bust."

"He asked me if I was ready to climb the corporate ladder."

"I'm not worried ... that little weasel doesn't have the guts to fire me."

"Listen, kid, I'm sure management would tell us if there was a problem."

"Our extended warranty covers everything except parts and labor."

"I like your use of dividends, and especially this payroll motif!"

"We're looking for a celebrity endorsement."

"Here's the history book I borrowed."

"... and that's our profit for this quarter."

"Where did you say you got your communications degree?"

"I suggest we sell all our assets and buy lottery tickets."

"You mean, you've been locked in this stairway for three years?"

"C'mon kid, nobody rolls their own anymore."

"You can call me Bob."

"Just two more gallons and we get a free set of steak knives."

"I didn't think they could screw you this way."

"That's what I like about you, sir — there are no gray areas."

"I think it's time we reviewed our corporate strategy."

"Well, we found your suitcase. And is our face red."

"This microchip is replacing you, Figwood. But if it makes you feel better, it doesn't work either."

"Mr. McMullen says you can come back when you say you're sorry."

"We're out of the closet and ready to change the world!"

"They overbook every time I fly."

"When I told him we missed the deadline, he became unglued."

"Sure, we have an incentive plan — if you screw up, you're fired!"

"I remember when you didn't need a college degree."

"... and just when I was about to give up on this company."

"Why do people who work sitting down make more money than those standing up."

"I think these teamwork seminars are finally working!"

"Bob, could you pick me up after work? And bring your wet suit."

Corporate Siberia.

"We can't print this, Frank. It's too close to the truth."

"Keep a sharp eye — somebody here is stealing office supplies."

"Honey, do we have any elbow grease?"

"I told you never to call me at work."

"After 25 years, this stuff still cracks me up."

"You know, of course, this will go on your permanent record."

"I've always wanted an office with a view."

"On Dasher! On Prancer! Or I'll contract out!"

MANAGER
1st ASST. MANAGER
2nd ASST. MANAGER
MAIL ROOM CLERK

WAISGLASS/COULTHART

"It just says that if I fail to win your case, I get first rights to your ribs and loin."

"You know, carpentry wasn't my first career choice."

"We make jackets. What did you think we do?"

"This high-performance computer has only one crucial flaw ..."

"Milner, we finally found a job for you that doesn't require computer training."

"Sorry, Brimswell, you've been traded to Accounting for three calculators and a fax machine."

**"Don't worry, Bob.
Mr. Flatch respects honesty."**

"Next time you do that, you're fired."

**"I love you, but you never
take me anywhere."**

"It's for a good cause."

"Don't be silly, it's not a *real* human."

"Payroll will be ready in a few minutes."

"But you said I should get a summer job."

"Geez, I had no idea there was a Nobel Prize for accounting."

WAISGLASS/COULTHART

"Not too hard this time — the last idea gave me a concussion."

"Wow, how did you know I wanted my fortune told?"

"This floor plan was favored by 96% of the laboratory rats tested."

"This ought'a make it more sporting."

It wasn't exactly what he expected, but finally Harold's ship came in.

"These marches always attract fringe groups."

"Sorry about the flambé. Would you like me to fill your glass while I'm here?"

The first layoff.

"We wanted to improve our image."

"It's not a bad job, but I hate the hours."

"Don't chat with the customers — it scares them."

"No matter how cold it is outside, never go into a liquor store wearing a ski mask."

"Pedal faster, Millwood — the lights are dimming."

"Well, this should take care of the job stress I was having."

"Now Tom, you agree to warm your hands before milking ... and Janet, you promise not to wander."

"This explains the low membership fees."

"Does this seem a little too easy?"

"Good news ... I've negotiated a settlement that should cover your legal fees."

"I hope Lou's Liquor Store gets hit again. Last nights ratings sky-rocketed."

"Do you have an account with us?"

"Say, Frank, isn't that your cow that's wandered on the road."

"He forgot to pay the bill."

"You got 25 years for a system error?"

"Yeah, we heard it up here too!"

"And the first party of the first part, herein known as Cathy ..."

"Wow! Cool earrings, Dad."

"Let me assure you, sir, I will personally seek out the calculator responsible for those errors."

"But you'll miss 'Seinfeld'!"

HERD
FREE THINKERS
WAISGLASS/COULTHART

"I'm not here to rescue you, Mr. Harris — I'm your wife's attorney."

"She doesn't really work here, but it's one heck of a deterrent."

"She wants us to wipe our feet."

"And for your personal comfort and safety, we recommend you do not eat our in-flight meal."

"Your contract is trading three points higher than yesterday."

"My chiropractor says I should find a branch that's more ergonomically correct."

"He says he likes to work with people."

"We must be on a mailing list."

"Should I hold your calls?"

"If there was an embezzler here,
I'd know about it!"

"I'm here to apply for the job."

"In other words, *smile* while
you're being screwed."

"I can assure you, we've never had a complaint."

"You misspelled 'graduate'."

"This is no ordinary cat."

"I don't like it either, but we've got to evolve as a species."

"One extra large guy, no onions."

"It's people like you who give this business a bad name."

"I need a leave of absence."

"Stop this sacred cow stuff before it affects the entire herd."

"So, you went to Harvard and learned to delegate authority, then what happened?"

"The network is down and my computer keeps saying 'union, union, union'."

"It sort of sells itself — doesn't it?"

"Congratulations, Mr. Rouse, you're now a free agent!"

JACK
ESTIMATE
JACK'S PLUMBING
WAISGLASS/COULTHART

"... and how much do they have in their pension plan?"

Just before lunch, Marvin learns about the process of natural selection.

"Is it me, or does the day seem to drag on forever?"

"Maybe you didn't notice, kid, but we have a dress code here."

"It says, 'For a good time, call Cleo'."

"I have the technology to communicate with the world, but I have nothing to say."

"Geez, I hate tax law."

"I empowered my employees, and then they laid me off because I was redundant."

"Sure, we're over managed, but we can't afford to make mistakes."

"Do you have any experience working in the public sector?"

WAISGLASS/COULTHART

"They've got to do something about all this violence on TV."

"Your account must be overdrawn."

"How did a cute little tax deduction turn into a major liability."

"Get out there and improve morale or you're fired!"

"He tends to over-simplify."

"Let's not panic — this may be just a coincidence."

"I want to protect my intellectual property."

"There's another manager caught in the machinery."

"I'd rather have the raise."

"Your doorbell must be broken."

"We wanted our lawyers to cut the cake."

"It must be one of those infomercials."

"Say, let's give old Grizwald a wedgie."

"Do you have flexible hours? I don't usually get up before noon."

"Okay, nobody panic. Nurse, hand me a scalpel, a really long spoon and some chocolate sprinkles."

"It's from Joey. He'll be in law school another 3 to 5 years."

"They wanted to improve top-down communications."

"Do you have anything I can rent?"

"We've been told to balance the budget."

"It's just a lot of bologna with a slice of ham."

"I'm sorry, Mr. Finlay, but your medical plan doesn't cover everything."

"As your lawyer, I must insist you avoid any action that may prevent you from paying your legal bills."

"Man, those guys on Cloud Nine have all the fun."

"Uh, there's still the small matter of my fee ..."

"I'm telling you, this ship is dangerously top-heavy."

"I know it's a bargain, but going south in the off-season goes against my better instincts.

"Uh, it seems we lost our list of demands."

"Mr. Gorman is our new Director of Personnel."

"Don't give up, Henry — these bill collectors let go eventually."

"I know the herd follows you, Betsy, but I doubt they're ready to strike."

"To his horror, Dr. Jekyll realizes he has turned himself into an administrator."

"Pay your bill, pay your bill ..."

"Suspended with pay — and you?"

"Geez, do they always turn white like that?!"

"Settle down, Slim. You knew we were playing for big steaks."

ACME
SHARP
STICKS